KT-546-874

mindbending

lateral puzzles

Publisher: Simon Melhuish
Editor: Nikole Bamford
Puzzle Compilers: Lloyd King, Rich Garner, Jenny Lynch
Additional Contributors: Sarah Wells, Peter Sorenti, Jane Purcell, Sue Curran
Designer: Al Shiner
Contributing Designer: Sarah Wells

Published by:
LAGOON BOOKS
PO Box 311, KT2 5QW, UK
PO Box 990915, Boston, MA 02199, USA

www.thelagoongroup.com

ISBN 978-1-906170-83-7

Printed in China

mindbending

lateral puzzles

The Original and Best!

All New Edition!

INTRODUCTION

All the mindbending puzzle books have been carefully compiled to give the reader a refreshingly wide range of challenges, some requiring only a small leap of perception, others deep and detailed thought. All the books share an eye-catching and distinctive visual style that presents each problem in an appealing and intriguing way. Do not, however, be deceived; what is easy on the eye is not necessarily easy on the mind!

A woman watched her husband plunge head first down a deep ravine. She returned home to find him in the kitchen, chopping onions. How is this possible?

Detective Sergeant Smith turned up at the station slightly later than he intended. He didn't start working, he just looked at his watch, sighed and went home. His chief wasn't a stickler for punctuality – why the change in heart?

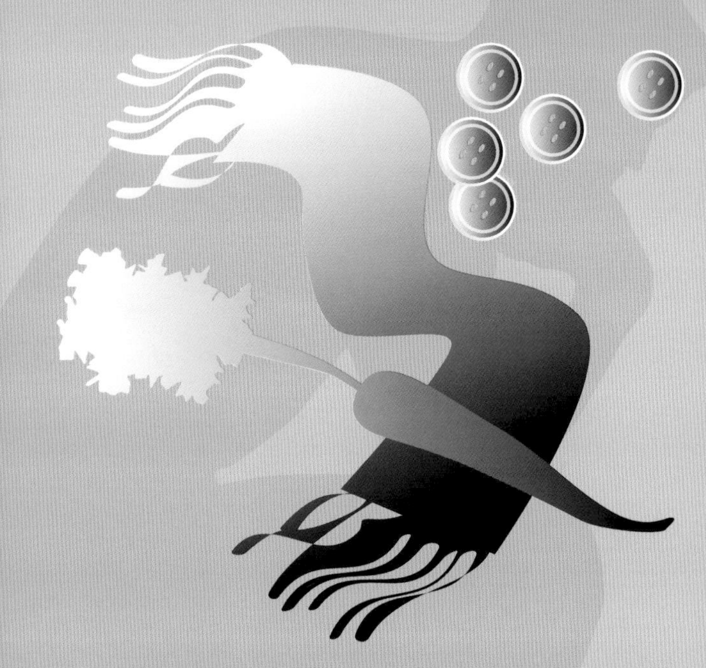

A carrot, a scarf and five buttons were found in a field. If nobody placed them there, how did they get there?

My friend Sarah told me that her

grandmother

was younger than her

mother.

Could this be true?

Dave ran halfway into the forest in half an hour. Steve claimed he had gone two-thirds of the way into the forest in the same time, but Dave said that was impossible. Why?

One morning a gas station attendant ran into the office the moment his boss arrived, and told him that the previous evening he had dreamt that one of the pumps had been leaking, causing a huge explosion. His boss was skeptical, but when he checked the pump in question, he indeed found a potentially disastrous leak. He switched off the pump and then sacked the attendant. Why?

On the table is a carton containing six eggs.
If six people each take one egg, how can it be that one egg is left in the carton?

When asked who a certain photograph was of, the owner replied:

'I have neither sister nor brother, but my mother's daughter is that man's mother.'

Who was in the photograph?

If it rained for 40 days and 40 nights, and the animals entered in pairs at a rate of 30 pairs per day, how many days did it take Moses to get all 360 animals onto the ark?

A man stopped his car at a hotel and immediately knew he was bankrupt. How?

A man returned his soup to the restaurant kitchen because there was a dead fly floating in it. When the waiter returned with a new bowl of soup, the diner was incensed to discover that it was exactly the same soup, simply with the fly removed.
How did he know?

Mr Robinson wanted a house where all the windows in all of the rooms faced south. How did he manage this?

A horse plows a field all day. If he takes 24 steps to reach from one edge of the field to the other, how many hoof prints will the horse leave in the last furrow.

Why are

1984

bottles of whiskey more valuable than

1977

bottles of whiskey?

An ordinary American citizen, with no passport, visits over 30 foreign countries in one day. He is welcomed in each country and leaves each one of his own accord. How is this possible?

Detective Smith finds Romeo and Juliet dead on the kitchen floor surrounded by broken glass. They were alone when they died. What killed them?

A woman was halfway up an escalator when she suddenly began to weep.

Why?

An airplane carrying 60 Mexican lawyers to a convention in Rio crashed and landed directly on the border between Colombia, Venezuela and Brazil. Under international law, where should the survivors be buried.

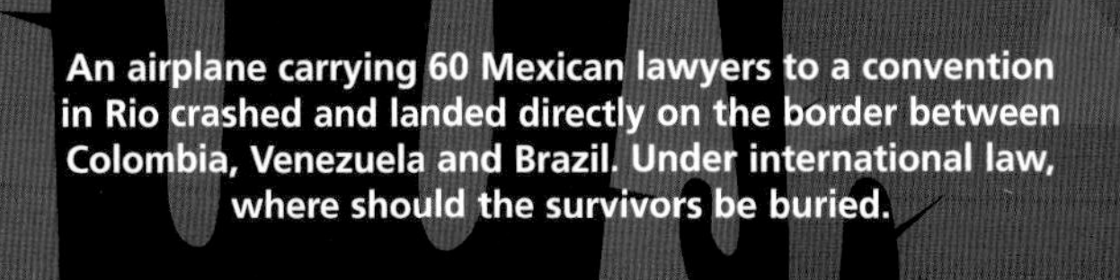

In 1987 a crane

collapsed

in a residential area of Liverpoool at lunchtime yet nobody saw or heard a thing.

Why not?

EAST

WEST

Two hitch-hikers were waiting for a lift, watching for passing cars. One was looking east towards the mountains, and the other west towards the sea. 'You're looking a bit rough this morning,' said the first one to the other. How could he tell?

A man looks out the window.
He is desperate to open it, yet he knows this would kill him. Why?

Two men are seated at a table. Neither has spoken for one and a half hours. There is no-one else in the room. Suddenly, one of them shouts with glee and leaps up before collapsing with an agonised yell. What has happened?

How many mice are in a box if there is a mouse in each corner, and opposite each mouse there are three mice and at each mouse's tail there is a mouse.

When the police discovered the body of Colonel Reginald Smith, they found a tape recorder and gun by his side. On starting the tape they heard a suicide message, closely followed by the sound of a pistol being fired. Without hesitation the police handed over the case to the murder squad. Why?

Tom and Ella emerged from playing in the cellar. Tom had a clean face, but Ella had a dirty smear on her forehead. Why was it Tom who went to wash?

Seven men were traveling along a lane. It began to rain. Six of the men quickened their step and got wet. The seventh man did not quicken his step but remained quite dry. He had neither hat nor umbrella so how did he stay dry?

A woman is out shopping. At one point, she stops, searches in her bag for a coin, and puts it in a slot. She sighs and begins to search for another coin. Suddenly she stops, takes off her coat, and then deposits the second coin. Thoroughly disgruntled, she puts her coat back on and walks away. What has just happened?

You can use
three identical digits
in a simple addition sum
so that the total is 12.
You cannot use the digit 4
so what is the answer?

When is it more polite to pass or overtake on the inside?

Polly Warden loved the color yellow. All the walls in her new bungalow were primrose yellow. The carpets, curtains and all the soft furnishings were a golden yellow. What color were the stairs.

Two parachutists
drift off course.
When they land
one walks north,
the other walks south
yet within an hour
they meet up.
Explain.

A doctor and police surgeon were comparing notes on a case. The doctor explained that a man had fallen asleep while at the cinema. The horror film he had been watching obviously influenced his dream.

He dreamt that he was being chased through a deserted castle by a beast with two heads. He ran to the top of the tower and found himself looking down a large drop into a crocodile-infested moat. Behind him he could hear the beast's roar as it made its way up the stairs towards him. Just as he had to turn and face the beast, his wife shook him to waken him.

The shock was so great for the poor man that he immediately collapsed and died.

'That's absolute nonsense,'

cried the surgeon. How was he so sure?

A father and son were involved in a car accident and rushed to hospital. On seeing the unconscious young boy, the surgeon exclaimed, 'Oh no, that's my son.' How can this be true?

Why did a man, standing alone in a house, suddenly raise his hands in the air, laugh, let his hands drop and then leave the building?

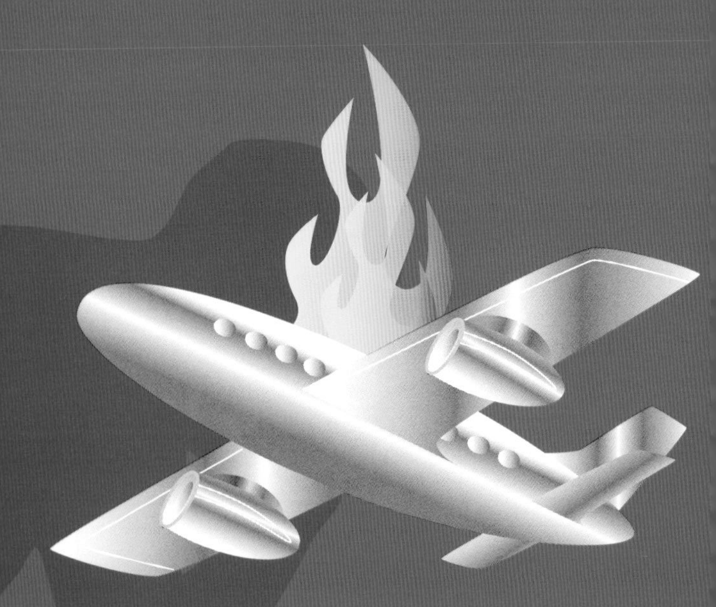

When a fire broke out on an airplane, a panicking passenger opened the emergency hatch and threw himself out, even though he had no parachute. How was it that when the rescue services found him, he was alive and well and without injury?

The maker does not need it,
the buyer does not use it
and the user uses it
without knowing.
What is it?

A completely naked man robs a newspaper kiosk, and then runs off into the crowd.
The police are unable to find him, and all the witnesses have trouble describing him. Explain.

Following a tip-off, a team of FBI agents burst into a house to arrest a suspected murderer. All they know is that his name is Bud. They find two plumbers, a truck driver and a bank manager playing poker in a dark and smoky room. They immediately arrest the bank manager. Why?

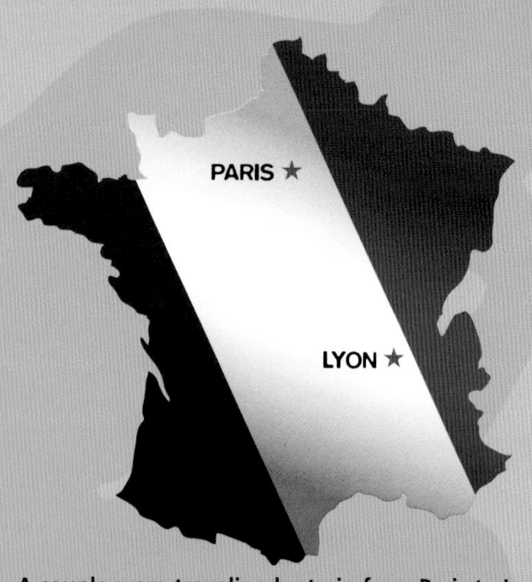

A couple were traveling by train from Paris to Lyon. The woman went to the buffet car, and on her return discovered her partner had leapt to his death. Only a handkerchief remained in the compartment. The woman was distraught, knowing that if they had taken another route he would still be alive. What happened?

A man died on January 23rd, yet was buried on January 22nd. Why the premature burial?

R.I.P.

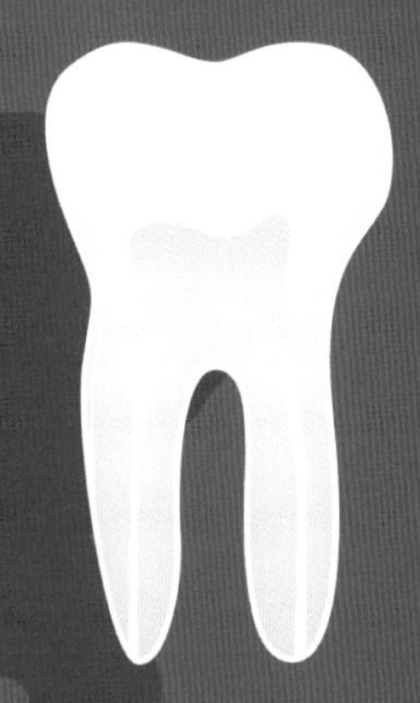

A woman had just moved to a new area and needed some dental work done. There were two dentists in the town and she visited them both. The first had a brand new surgery, he looked very well-presented and had excellent teeth. The second had bad teeth, an untidy surgery and was in a bad mood due to chronic toothache.
Why did the woman register with the second dentist?

The guard of an open prison was given strict instructions not to allow any prisoner to leave the prison without release papers, or to allow any visitor into the prison without written permission from the governor. The guard watched over a strip of land which was the only way into or out of the prison. He knew it would take at least 9–10 minutes for anyone to cross the land and so checked it every 5 minutes. How did a prisoner make a successful escape, despite having no release papers?

A basketball player lay dead in his driveway next to his mailbox having shot himself. On closer inspection the police realized that the mailbox was connected to his death, and that this was a murder investigation. What did they discover?

CRIMINAL

If a man cannot be tried for the same crime twice, why was Edward Dukes tried six times last week for the murder of Lady Soames?

One Friday morning two trains speed along the same track through an empty railway station. One is heading north, the other south. Neither train brakes, nor diverts to another track, yet they avoid a collision. How?

A princess is kidnapped by her cruel uncle, who has planned for her to marry one of his two sons. He gave her an ultimatum – she was to make a solitary statement. If what she said was true, she was to marry her elder cousin Johans the Vain. However, if what she said was false, she would marry the younger son, Derek the Dismal.
What did she say which allowed her to remain single?

A group of seven people arrived at a hotel late one night and asked for seven rooms. The hotelier actually only had six rooms available but said he would try to help. He put the first person in the first room and asked the second to wait a moment. He put the third person in the second room, the fourth in the third room and the fifth in the fourth room.

Finally he placed the sixth person in the fifth room, went back for the seventh person and put them in the sixth room.

Satisfied?

Captain Cabbage RN of HMS Slaughter woke one morning to find he had a black eye. Initially he considered court martialing the duty officer responsible, but instead he decided to put plastic wrap over the officer's toilet seat. Why?

I often go to the police station in the middle of night and destroy hundreds of fingerprints. I do not, however, consider myself a criminal. Who am I?

A farmer is walking across his land when he comes upon a bundle. A few feet away he is horrified to discover the body of a dead man. Immediately the farmer knew how the man had met his death. How?

The police arrested a suspected murderer; they found a blood-stained knife in the outside right pocket of his jacket. When the forensic team went to pick up the evidence the knife was on the inside left-hand pocket. Nobody had touched the jacket so how did it turn up in a different place?

A prisoner was made to carry a heavy sandbag from one side of the compound to the other. When he got to the other side, he had to take it back again. This went on hour after hour, day after day, until the prisoner realized he could put something in the bag to make it lighter. What was it?

I'm inside,
halfway up a building
that has no windows
or balconies, yet
I have an incredible
view of the city.
How come?

The soccer manager was talking to his team after the match and pointed at Johnson, who was one of the laziest, most inept players on the pitch and said, 'If only we had five players like him.' Has he gone mad?

Sheriff Tom Jones rode into town on Friday, stayed three nights and left early on Sunday morning. Explain.

I picked up my long lost uncle from Alaska at the airport. I had never seen a picture of him nor met him or heard him described, yet I recognized him immediately. How?

I went into France with something that stopped
when we got to the airport.
Despite this, it was still with me when I returned.
What is it?

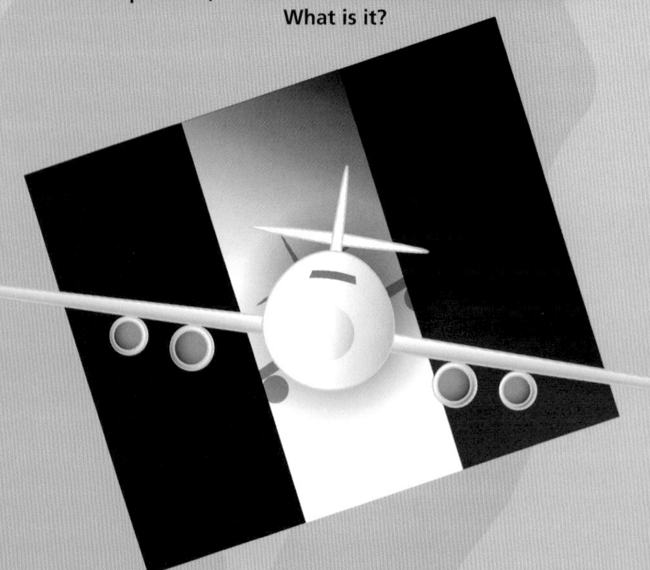

When the family jewels were stolen from inside a vat of oil and vinegar, my brother suspected my sister's widow. How did I know this was wrong?

A man walks into a well-lit room and flicks the switch. The lights flicker, and the man leaves, contented. Why?

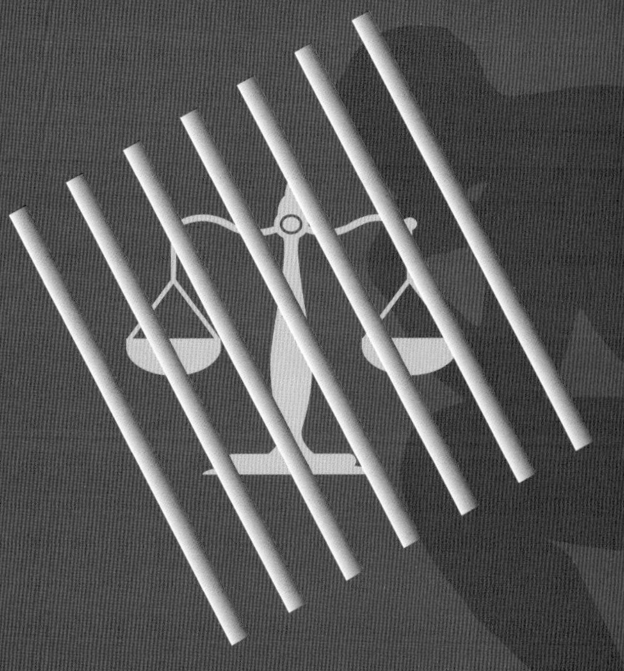

A prisoner survived in a cell with no water and a thick steel door between him and a fresh water well outside in the courtyard. How?

If I stand on the end of my tie and you stand on the other end, how will we not be able to touch each other?

A professional soccer player bet me that he could kick a ball a certain distance, have it stop and then come back to him without anything else touching it. How could he win the bet?

I was told by a magician to repeat 'lemon' three times.
I said 'lemon, lemon, lemon' whereupon he angrily said,
'Didn't you hear what said?'
What did I say wrong?

PRISONER BREAK OUT!

A prisoner is kept on 50 grains of rice and a bowl of water a day. Despite getting progressively weaker he manages to pull the bars from his window and escape after a year. How?

Dave looked under a table and saw a hand, completely detached from an arm.

He looked over at Alan, and although all his fingers and thumbs were in place, and his hands were attached to his arms, he knew the hand beneath the table must be his.

He stood up and punched Alan.

Why?

As I left the reptile house at the zoo I felt something in my pocket. I put my hand in and discovered something with no legs and several teeth. Once I knew what it was I left it there undisturbed. What was it?

What gets wetter as it dries?

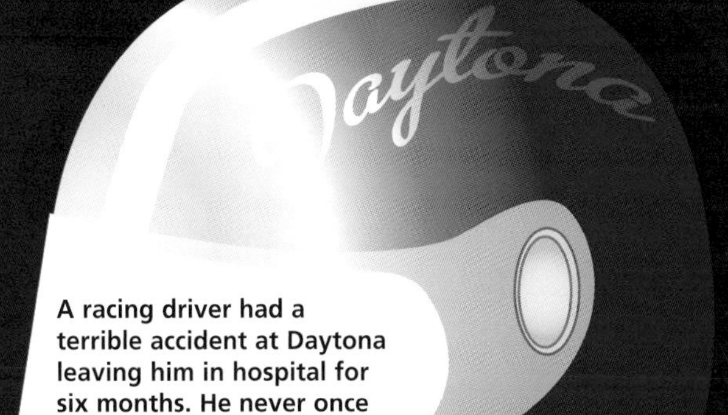

A racing driver had a terrible accident at Daytona leaving him in hospital for six months. He never once considered giving up racing. Why?

How can I stick a pin in a balloon without making a noise or the balloon releasing air?

Umbro The Unnatural

It was 3.30pm and sinister magician
Umbro the Unnatural was standing in the middle of a
park. There were no trees or buildings round him and
not a cloud in the sky, yet he cast no shadow.
How did he do this?

A man is killed by a
pane of glass.
The glass didn't fall on him,
and it wasn't broken
before it killed him.
So how did he die?

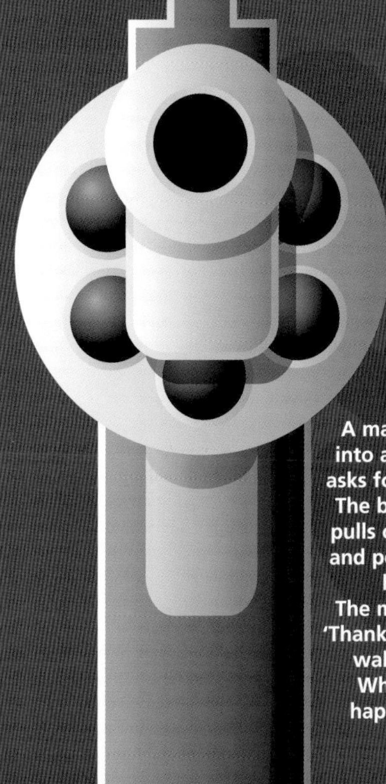

A man walks into a bar and asks for a drink. The bartender pulls out a gun and points it at him. The man says, 'Thank you,' and walks out. What has happened?

A man is found hanging in an otherwise empty locked room with a puddle of water under his feet. How did he die?

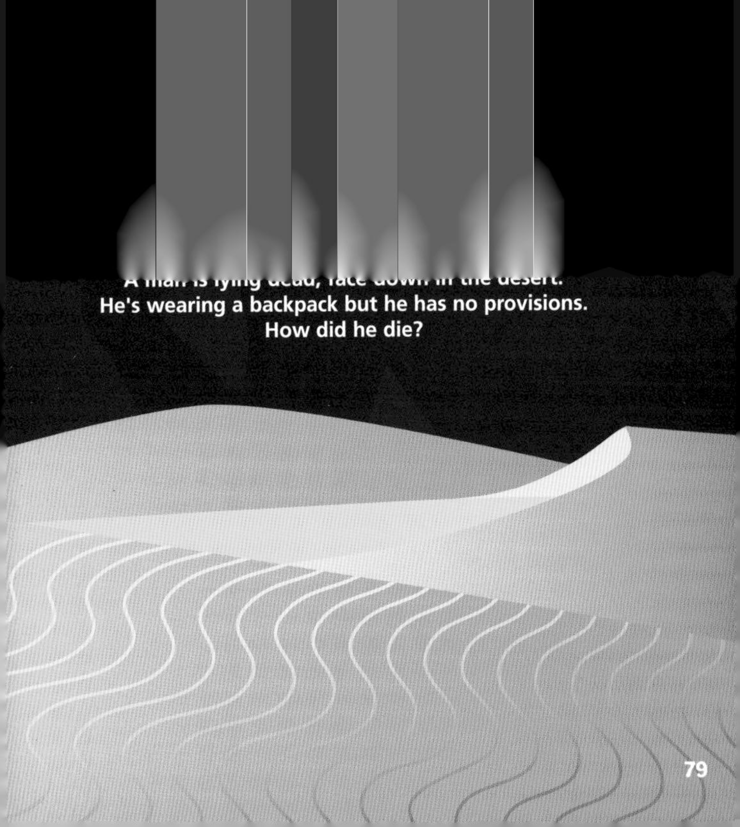

A man is lying dead, face down in the desert.
He's wearing a backpack but he has no provisions.
How did he die?

A man is driving his car. He turns on the radio, listens for five minutes, turns around, goes home and shoots his wife. Why?

A MAN IS LYING AWAKE IN BED. HE MAKES A PHONE CALL, SAYS NOTHING AND GOES TO SLEEP. WHY?

A man gets onto an elevator. When the elevator stops, he knows his wife is dead. How?

A man is running along a corridor with a piece of paper in his hand. Explain why, when the lights flicker, does the man drop to his knees and cry out

an tries to drop a
man into
by his own request – but
lows back in.

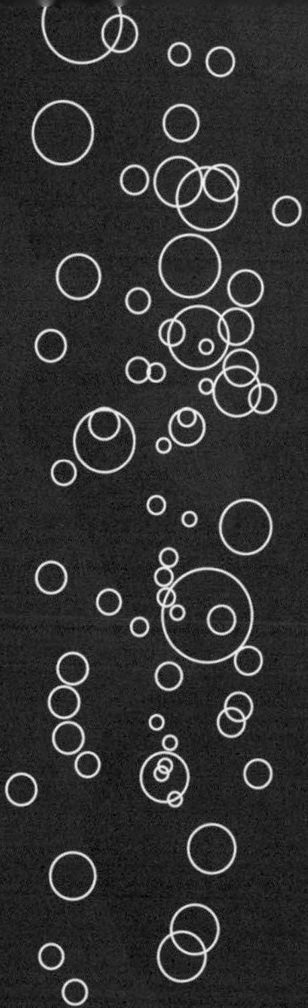

A man wakes up one night to get some water. He turns off the light and goes back to bed. The next morning he looks out the window, screams and kills himself. What has he done to make him kill himself?

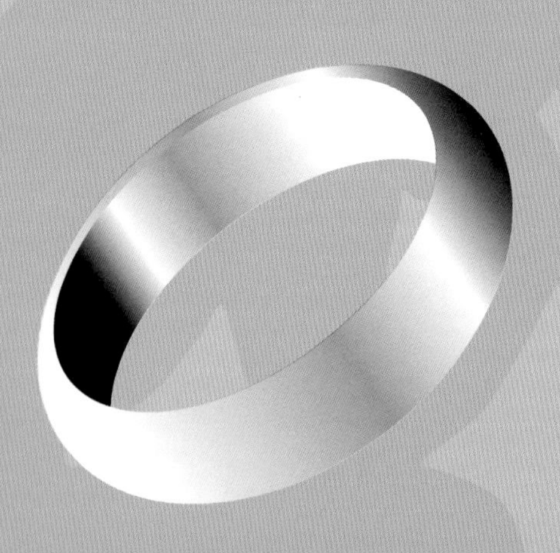

A woman grabbed a man's ring, pulled on it and dropped it, thereby saving his life. How was his life saved?

Page 6
Her husband was a stuntman and she had been watching him on TV.

Page 7
It was a train station, it was his day off and he'd missed the train.

Page 8
They are the remains of a snowman after the snow has melted.

Page 9
Yes. Her paternal grandmother could be younger than her own mother.

Page 10
You can only run halfway into a forest. After that you're running out of the forest.

Page 11
The attendant had been on the night shift and should not have been asleep.

Page 12
The last person leaves the egg in the carton.

Page 13
It was the owner's son.

Page 14
None. It was Noah's Ark.

Page 15
He was playing Monopoly.

Page 16
He had seasoned the soup with lots of pepper before seeing the dead fly.

Page 17
He built a house on the North Pole so all the sides face south.

Page 18
None. The plow will turn the soil over and cover any hoof prints left by the animal.

Page 19
Because there are seven more bottles of whiskey. The numbers are quantities, not dates.

Page 20
He is a mail courier who delivers packages to the different foreign embassies in the United States. The land of an embassy belongs to the country of the embassy, not to the United States.

Page 21
Romeo and Juliet were goldfish and their bowl was knocked over by a cat.

Page 22
The escalator was in a hospital where she was visiting her husband in intensive care. A power failure caused the escalator to stop, meaning that her husband's life support machine would have stopped working.

Page 23
You do not bury survivors.

Page 24
The crane was a bird.

Page 25
They were facing each other.

Page 26
He is in a submarine suffering from claustrophobia.

Page 27
The two men were playing chess. Having finally achieved checkmate one of them leapt to his feet in glee – only to discover his leg had gone dead.

Page 28
Four mice, each one near the tail of the mouse in the adjacent corner.

Page 29
Because the tape was already rewound ready for them to listen to it.

Page 30
They looked at each other. The clean child saw the other's dirty face and assumed he was as dirty. The dirty child assumed she was as clean as the other.

Page 31
The six men were pallbearers. The seventh was in the coffin.

Page 32
The woman stepped on a weighing machine in a pharmacy. She removed her coat to see if she weighed less but it didn't work.

Page 33
11 + 1 = 12

Page 34
On a spiral staircase where the insides are narrower and hence harder to climb.

Page 35

There are no stairs in a bungalow.

Page 36

They didn't drift off course together, but landed two hours' walk away from each other.

Page 37

If the man died so quickly then she wouldn't know what he was dreaming.

Page 38

The surgeon was the boy's mother.

Page 39

The man was a burglar who raised his hands on the words 'Stop, thief.' When he realized these words were uttered by the pet parrot in a cage he relaxed, laughed and made a hasty retreat.

Page 40

The airplane was on the ground when he leapt.

Page 41

A coffin.

Page 42

The kiosk was in a naturist resort.

Page 43

The only man was the bank manager.

Page 44

The man had been treated for blindness and was wearing the handkerchief to rest his eyes. When alone, he took it off but unfortunately the train was going through a tunnel at the time. He thought he had lost his sight again and jumped to his death in despair.

Page 45

The man died in Fiji and the body was flown to Western Samoa for burial. The flight crossed the International Date Line from West to East and would arrive in effect the previous day.

Page 46

If there are only two dentists in town then they must treat each other's teeth. Therefore the dentist with bad teeth had looked after the other dentist.

Page 47

When the guard was in his hut the prisoner walked for five minutes towards freedom then turned around and started to walk towards the prison. When he reached the guard he did not have any permission paper to enter so the guard sent him back – to his freedom!

Page 48

Every night a rival basketball player added a bit of wood to the post of the mailbox. After a week the player was convinced he was shrinking. Desolate at the thought of losing his livelihood, he committed suicide.

Page 49

Edward was a character in a theatrical production.

Page 50

They go through at different times.

Page 51

She said 'I will marry Derek the Dismal.' If her uncle did marry her off to Derek the statement would have been true so he should have married her to Johans instead. But if he married her to Johnans then her statement would have been false. The uncle has to let her go.

Page 52
The second person still has no room.

Page 53
On washing his face the black eye disappeared. The captain was the victim of a prank and then responded with another practical joke.

Page 54
The police station cleaner.

Page 55
The bundle is an unopened parachute which failed to open thus the man died.

Page 56
The jacket was reversible and when the police removed the coat it had turned inside out.

Page 57
A hole.

Page 58
The building is made of glass.

Page 59
He hasn't gone mad but the team has played a disastrous game and might have fared better with only five inept players rather than the whole team.

Page 60
Friday is the name of his horse.

Page 61
He is my father's identical twin.

Page 62
A watch.

Page 63
My sister can't have a widow.

Page 64
He's an executioner and came in to test the electric chair which made the lights flicker.

Page 65
The door wasn't locked.

Page 66
If the tie is threaded under a door we wouldn't be able to touch each other.

Page 67
He kicked it straight in the air.

Page 68
If I repeated 'lemon' three times I should have said it four times: lemon, lemon, lemon lemon. If he'd told me to repeat lemon once, I would have said it twice.

Page 69
Every day he saves and dries out a couple of grains of rice, puts them in the cracks around the bars and puts some water on them. Gradually the swelling increases the size of the cracks loosening the bars.

Page 70
They were playing cards and the 'hand' under the table was a duplicate set of cards, proving that Alan was cheating.

Page 71
A comb.

Page 72
A towel.

Page 73
It wasn't a car-related accident; he fell down some stairs.

Page 74
The balloon isn't inflated.

Page 75

It was a winter's afternoon in Scandinavia and it was already dark.

Page 76

He fell through the glass from a great height, rather than it falling on him.

Page 77

The man has hiccups; the bartender scares them away by pulling a gun.

Page 78

He stood on a block of ice to hang himself.

Page 79

He jumped out of an airplane, but his parachute failed to open.

Page 80

The radio program is one of those shows where they call up someone at random and ask them a question. The announcer states the name and town of the man's wife as the person he would call next. He does so, and a male voice answers. From this, he gathers his wife is having an affair.

Page 81

He is in a hotel and is unable to sleep because the man in the adjacent room is snoring. He calls the snorer up (at this hotel, like many others, the phone numbers are based on the room number). The snorer wakes up and answers. The first man hangs up without saying anything and goes to sleep before the snorer starts snoring again.

Page 82

He's leaving a hospital after visiting his wife, who's on a life support system. The power goes out, stopping the elevator and, he guesses, the life support system, too. (He assumes if the emergency back-up generator were working, the elevator wouldn't lose power either.)

Page 83

The man is delivering a pardon, and the flicker of the lights indicates that the person to be pardoned has just been electrocuted.

Page 84

The man has been cremated. The woman is his wife. Before his death, he requested that his ashes be scattered on the ocean. But it's a windy day, and his ashes blow back on the boat.

Page 85

The man is a lighthouse keeper. He isn't quite awake when he gets up in the night – unwittingly, he shuts off the light in the lighthouse. During the night, a ship crashes on the rocks. When the man realizes what he has done, he kills himself.

Page 86

The man and woman were skydiving. The man broke his arm as he jumped from the plane by hitting it on the plane door, and he couldn't reach his ripcord with his other arm. The woman pulled the ripcord for him.

Other titles in the Mindbending range include:

Mindbending Conundrums

Mindbending Logic Puzzles

Mindbending Speed Puzzles

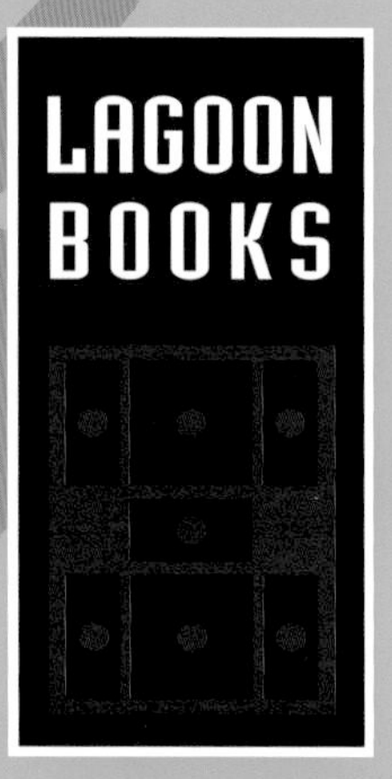